The Wind in the Willows

Kenneth Grahame

Simplified by Sue Ullstein
Illustrations by Ernest H Shepard

Longman Group UK Limited,
Longman House, Burnt Mill, Harlow,
Essex CM20 2JE, England
and Associated Companies throughout the world.

This simplified edition © Longman Group UK Limited 1987

First published 1987

ISBN 0-582-54142-5

Set in 12/14 point Linotron 202 Versailles
Produced by Longman Group (FE) Limited
Printed in Hong Kong

Acknowledgements

Line illustrations by Ernest H Shepard copyright under the
Berne Covention. In the United States copyright 1933 Charles
Scribner's Sons, renewal copyright © 1961 Ernest H Shepard.
Copyright in colouring-in © 1970, 1971 by Ernest H Shepard
and Methuen Children's Books Limited.

The cover background is a wallpaper design called NUAGE,
courtesy of Osborne and Little plc.

Stage 2: 900 word vocabulary

Please look under *New words* at the back of this book
for explanations of words outside this stage.

Contents

Introduction

Introduction

Kenneth Grahame

The writer of this book, Kenneth Grahame, was born in Scotland in 1859. He went to school in Oxford, did very well there, and so got work in the Bank of England. He was successful, and he became the Secretary of the Bank of England, with his name printed on all banknotes.

Kenneth Grahame was rather like Badger in this book, not really liking parties and places where there were "a lot of people". But he loved children, and life in the countryside, and the small wild creatures that live there.

Before *The Wind in the Willows* he wrote two books for and about children: *The Golden Age* (1895) and *Dream Days* (1898). Although they were children's books, grown-ups loved them, and they are still read and enjoyed today by grown-ups as well as children.

The Wind in the Willows

This book – again for children, but loved by grown-ups – was probably Grahame's best. It appeared in 1908, with drawings by Ernest Shepard, who had drawn pictures for *Punch* magazine, and later drew the children and toy animals for A.A. Milne's *Winnie the Pooh* and *The House at Pooh Corner*.

In *The Wind in the Willows*, the four friends, Water Rat, Mole, Toad and Badger behave rather like very small human beings. But at the same time they see things with the eyes of small animals. They are very good friends.

It may be useful to have a description of the animals as they really are, but remember that in the book they are only partly animals:

A *water rat*, or vole, makes its home in a hole in a river bank. It is about 10 to 20 centimetres long including a short tail, and its colour is usually a dark grey-brown.

A *mole* makes tunnels under the ground. It is about the same size as a water rat, sometimes rather larger. Its eyes are not good, but its strong front feet help it to tunnel quickly, finding insects and worms for food.

A *toad* is rather like a frog, but its skin is rough. Usually a toad doesn't jump like a frog; sometimes it seems to walk. It is quite small – about 5 to 8 centimetres long. Toads usually live on dry land.

A *badger* is much bigger than a water rat or a mole, up to 75 centimetres long, not including a short tail. It comes out of its underground home mostly at night, and it keeps away from people.

Toad, Rat and Mole with their caravan (see page 13)

Chapter 1
The river bank

The Mole had been working hard all morning. It was spring and he was cleaning his house after the winter. He lived under the ground but he knew spring had come. Suddenly, he wanted to stop. He had done enough cleaning for one day! So he climbed up his tunnel – up! up! – to the ground. Mole breathed the fresh spring air. How good it smelled! Then he jumped out of his hole and started walking. Where was he going? He didn't know. He just liked being outside. Everywhere animals were spring cleaning. He enjoyed watching them work. He was happy that he had finished cleaning.

He walked for a long time. Then suddenly he saw something new. He had never seen anything like it – it was a river. It looked beautiful in the sunshine. Mole stood and watched it for a long time. Then he sat down on the bank. He noticed a dark hole in the bank on the other side of the river. Then he noticed two brown eyes inside the hole. The eyes moved and a head came out: it was the Water Rat.

"Hello, Mole!" said Water Rat.

"Hello, Rat!" said Mole.

"Would you like to come over here?" Rat asked next.

"Yes – but can I?" said Mole. He didn't know

about the river and he had never seen a boat.

"Of course you can!" laughed Rat. "Wait a minute. I'll come for you in my boat." And he got into a little blue and white boat which was outside his hole.

Mole was afraid when he first got into the boat, but he was also very excited. "So this is a real boat and I'm in it!" he thought to himself.

"This is a wonderful day!" he told Rat. "I've never been in a boat in my life."

"Never?" cried Rat. "You've ... never ...?" He was so surprised that he couldn't speak.

"Is boating really so nice?" asked Mole.

"Nice? It's the *nicest* thing in the world!" And Rat started to row across the river. "Look, Mole, have you got anything to do this morning? Because if you haven't, why don't we go out in the boat? We can take some food and go out on the river for the whole day."

Mole laughed happily. "Oh, Ratty. Let's start at once! This is the best day of my life!"

"Just a minute, then. I'll go and get some food," and Rat climbed into his hole. Two minutes later he came back. He was carrying a very large basket. "Here, Mole. Put this under your feet."

Rat took the oars and started to row. Mole sat back and looked at everything. It was all so beautiful: the sun on the water, the green of the banks and the gentle noise of the water on the bottom of the boat.

Rat gives Mole the food basket

Mole and Rat didn't speak for a long time. Then at last Mole said quietly, "So this is a river."

"*The* river," Rat said.

"And you live by the river, Rat – what a great life!" Mole went on.

"By it, with it, on it and in it," said Rat. "The river is my brother and sister, my mother and father, my friend, food and drink, and of course, washing! It's my world."

"But haven't you got any friends? If there's only you and the river, who do you talk to?" Mole wanted to know.

"Who do I talk to?" Rat laughed. "My dear Mole, there are a lot of people on the river bank. There are ducks, otters, toads, badgers – oh, hundreds of animals and birds. I've got a lot of friends."

"What's that over there, Ratty?" asked Mole, and he pointed to a lot of dark trees about a mile away.

"Oh, that," said Rat. "That's the Wild Wood. We don't go there often. We like the river bank better."

"Why?" asked Mole. "Aren't the people in the Wild Wood very nice?"

"Well," said Rat slowly, "some of them are all right. Badger lives there and he's a good friend of mine. But some of the other animals, the stoats and weasels – well – I don't know them very well – but ..." and he stopped. Mole didn't ask any more questions about the Wild Wood.

He knew that it wasn't a very nice place.

"And what's on the other side of the Wild Wood?" Mole asked.

"The Wide World," answered Rat. "I've never been there and I'm never going there. And you mustn't go there. Now," he added, "here's the place for our lunch."

He rowed the boat down a little stream away from the big river. Everything there was quiet.

Rat helped Mole out of the boat on to the bank. Then he got out the food basket.

"Let's eat, Mole. Are you hungry?"

Mole was very hungry. He had had nothing to eat since breakfast many hours before.

They had a wonderful lunch and then they sat on the bank in the sunshine.

"What are you looking at?" Rat asked.

"I'm not sure," Mole answered. "I think there's something in the water, but I can't really see."

Suddenly there was a nose above the water. It was Otter.

"Why didn't you ask me to lunch, Ratty?" he cried when he saw the food basket.

"Well ..." said Rat. "Oh, Otter, this is my friend, Mr Mole."

"How do you do, Mole," said Otter.

"How do you do, Otter," said Mole.

"What a day this is," Otter went on. "The whole world's out. Spring really has come, hasn't it?"

There was a noise behind them and they saw another animal.

"Badger, what a surprise!" said Rat.

Badger walked two steps forward, but then he saw Otter and Mole. "Oh, a lot of people," he said quietly to himself. He turned round and walked away.

"Oh, Badger," said Rat. "He always does that. He doesn't like a lot of people. We shan't see him again today. Who's out on the river, Otter? Tell us."

"Toad's out. He's got a new rowing boat, new boating clothes – everything new." Otter looked at Rat and they both laughed.

"Once it was sailing," said Rat. "Then it was a houseboat and now it's rowing. Poor Toad, he never does anything for long. I wonder what will be next."

"He's such a nice person," said Otter, "but he really isn't safe in a rowing boat. Well, I must be going now."

"I really think we should go home, too, Mole," said Rat.

"Please let me row, Ratty," Mole said, as they got into the boat.

"No, Mole, not today. It isn't as easy as it looks. You must have some lessons first."

So Mole sat down. But after half an hour he tried again. This time he didn't say anything. He just got up, pushed Rat out of the way and took the oars.

Otter comes out of the water

"Stop it! Don't be silly," shouted Rat. "You can't row. You'll put us both in the river!"

But it was too late. Mole tried to row, and the next moment – SPLASH! The boat turned over and they were both in the water.

"Help!" thought Mole as he went down and down. "How cold it is! I think I'm going to die!" But suddenly he felt a hand. It pushed him to the bank. Rat had saved him. Poor Mole! He was so wet and cold and unhappy.

"Come on, Mole," said Rat. "Run up and down the bank. It will make you dry again. I'm going to get the boat."

Very soon everything was back in the boat and Rat rowed home.

"Ratty," said Mole quietly. "I'm really very sorry. I was very silly. I hope you'll forgive me. I won't do it again."

"Of course I'll forgive you, Mole," Rat answered. "What's a little water to a Water Rat? But, Mole, I think you should come and stay with me by the river. Then I can teach you to row and to swim."

"Oh, Ratty, thank you," said Mole. "That would be lovely." And he laughed for the first time since he had fallen into the water.

And so Mole went to stay at Rat's house. They had many happy days by the river, on the river and in the river. Mole learned to swim and to row. And he learned to love the river.

Chapter 2
Mole meets Toad

One warm summer morning Rat and Mole were sitting on the river bank.

"Ratty," said Mole. "Can we go and visit Toad? I've heard a lot about him and I'd like to meet him very much."

"Certainly, Mole," answered Rat. "Get the boat out and we'll go at once. Toad likes visitors – he'll be very glad to see us."

"Is Toad nice?" said Mole as they got into the boat.

"Yes, he is – very nice. Not very clever, perhaps, and sometimes he talks too much, but he's a good Toad."

Soon they saw Toad Hall from the river. It was a big, old house with a beautiful garden by the river. They left their little boat among Toad's boats. None of his boats were being used.

"I see," said Rat. "Boating is finished. I wonder what the latest thing is. Let's go and see."

They found Toad in the garden. He jumped up when he saw them.

"Ratty, how lovely to see you! I wanted to see you and here you are," he cried.

"Toad, this is my friend, Mole," said Rat. "Let's sit quietly for a moment, Toad," Rat went on. "Isn't this a beautiful place, Mole?"

9

Rat and Mole see Toad Hall from the river

Before Mole could answer, Toad cried, "Yes, it's the finest house on the river – or anywhere!"

Mole and Rat looked at each other and laughed. Toad noticed this and his face went red. "All right, Ratty. I know that I boast about my house, but it isn't a bad house, is it? Now, I need your help."

"If it's about your rowing," Rat said, "you're doing quite well, but you need some more lessons, I think."

"Oh, pooh – boating," Toad said. "Boating is for boys. It's a waste of time. No, I've found something better – something for the rest of my life. Come with me and I'll show you." He led Rat and Mole to the back of the house.

"There!" he said. "That's my new life." He pointed to a red and yellow caravan. "I'm going to travel everywhere in that caravan. I'll go to a new place every day. Come inside and see. There's everything we need."

Rat didn't want to go inside the caravan, but Mole was very excited. Toad showed him everything – the cooker, the little beds, the books, the games, the food. "I've remembered everything," he said at last. "When we start this afternoon, you'll see."

"Toad," said Rat slowly. "Did you say 'we' and 'start' and 'this afternoon'? Because I am not going to leave my river and my house and my boat. I am not going travelling. And you don't want to travel, do you, Mole?"

"Er, no, I don't," said Mole quietly. But the truth was that he really wanted to go. He had fallen in love with the little red and yellow caravan.

Rat could see that Mole wanted to go in the caravan. He didn't want to hurt his friend, so he said, "Shall we think about it for a time?"

"Yes," said Toad. "Let's think about it during lunch. You *will* stay for lunch, won't you?"

During lunch, Toad tried to change Rat's mind. He talked about his plans, and Mole was more and more excited. At last Rat said that they would go. "But only a short journey, Toad. Just a day or two."

Chapter 3
The open road

So the three friends left Toad Hall that afternoon. It was a lovely afternoon – warm sunshine, but not too hot. They travelled many miles and they saw a lot of new things. Late in the evening they stopped in a field. They had a simple meal while Toad talked about his plans for the next day.

"What a good life!" he said happily. "This is better than your river, Rat."

"No, it isn't," said Rat sadly.

"Oh, poor Rat," said Mole very quietly because he did not want Toad to hear. "Do you want to go home? We can leave very early in the morning if you like."

"No, no," answered Rat. "Thank you, but we must stay with Toad. It isn't safe to leave him. Don't worry. Caravanning won't last long. New things never last long with Toad."

But the end was nearer than Rat knew.

The next morning, Rat and Mole got up early, but they couldn't wake Toad. And so they washed the cups and plates, they cooked the breakfast and gave the horse some food. There was a lot of work, but Toad still slept. He didn't wake up until they had finished!

They had another good day outside. But on the second evening Mole and Rat made Toad help them. He didn't like helping very much.

The next day they were walking along a quiet road. Mole was leading the horse while Rat and Toad walked behind the caravan. Toad was talking a lot. Suddenly, in front of them there was a cloud of dust. It was coming towards them very fast. There was a lot of noise, too. "*Poop, poop!*" The next minute the cloud and the noise were on top of the animals. They couldn't see in the dust and they couldn't think because of the noise. They tried to jump out of the way, but they couldn't. In a minute the thing had passed them. Slowly the dust went away and the three animals could see each other again. The poor old horse was very frightened, and Mole had great difficulty holding him. The caravan was on its side in the road. The windows and two of the wheels were broken. What a sad sight it made!

Rat was very angry. He jumped up and down in the middle of the road. He shouted all the bad words he knew. Surprisingly, Toad did not seem to be angry. But he was behaving in a very unusual way. He was sitting in the middle of the road and he looked very happy. He said again and again, "Poop, poop! Poop, poop!"

"What *is* the matter with Toad?" Rat asked himself. "Why isn't he angry?"

"Come on, Toad," he said. "Help us with the caravan. Let's see if we can move it." But Toad still didn't move.

"What a wonderful sight!" he said quietly. "The only way to travel. So that is a motor car!"

The motor car in a cloud of dust

"What shall we do, Rat?" asked Mole. "The caravan is very badly broken. Toad must go to the police. He must tell them about that car."

"No," said Rat. "He won't go to the police. He has finished with caravans. Cars are the latest thing. I know. We must take him back to Toad Hall at once. Let's take the horse and walk to the next town. Then we can catch a train home."

And so Mole and Rat took Toad back to Toad Hall. Then they went back to Rat's house by the river. It was very late when they got there and they were very tired.

The next day they heard that Toad had gone up to London. He had bought a big new motor car!

Chapter 4
The Wild Wood

Mole had wanted to meet Badger for a long time. One day he said to Rat, "Why don't we ask Badger to dinner so that I can meet him?"

"No, I don't think so," Rat answered. "You see, Badger doesn't like dinner parties and things."

"Well, can't we go and visit *him*?" said Mole.

"No, Mole, we can't. We must wait until Badger comes to see us. He will come in the end. You'll see." And Rat would not say any more.

The summer passed quickly. Rat and Mole were very busy on the river every day. Then winter came and still Badger had not come to see them. Rat and Mole began to be lazy. They slept a lot, getting up late and going to bed early. Rat did very little during those short days. Sometimes he wrote little stories, but mostly he just sat by the fire. Often he and Mole talked about the past summer. And they remembered the good times that they had had.

Mole did not sleep as much as Rat, and one afternoon in the middle of winter he went out for a walk.

"I think I'll go and visit Mr Badger," he thought to himself. "It isn't really very far and Rat doesn't need me."

The country was very different in winter.

Everything looked dead. There were no leaves on the trees and the grass was brown. It was very cold. Mole walked quickly in order to keep warm. He arrived at the Wild Wood and walked straight in.

At first he didn't see anything frightening, but as he went deeper into the wood there was less light. As it got darker, poor Mole began to see strange faces in the blackness around him. Then he heard strange noises. He walked faster and faster. Day had become night. He was very frightened. There were more strange noises and the wood grew still darker. Mole didn't know which way to go. At last he stopped and found a hole under a big tree.

"I can't walk any more. I'm too tired and cold and frightened," he thought to himself. "I'll rest here. I think I'll be safe."

By this time Rat had woken up by his fire at home. "Teatime," he thought to himself. "Mole, shall we have some tea?" he shouted.

But there was no answer. Rat looked for Mole all over the house, but he couldn't find him. Then he saw that Mole's coat and winter shoes were not in their usual place.

"He's gone out," Rat thought. "I wonder where he's gone. Winter isn't a good time for walking." Suddenly Rat stopped. "Oh, no. I hope he hasn't gone to the Wild Wood!"

Rat quickly opened his front door and he could see the marks of Mole's winter shoes on

Mole in the Wild Wood

the ground. They were going towards the Wild Wood!

"I must go and find him at once. He doesn't know the Wild Wood and he'll be very frightened!" Rat cried.

It was already dark when Rat left home. He walked very quickly towards the Wild Wood. He didn't stop for a minute when he reached the wood. Every few minutes he called out, "Mole, Mole! Where are you? It's me – Rat!"

He walked for more than an hour but he couldn't find Mole. He was beginning to be afraid. He thought something had happened to Mole.

Suddenly, when he thought he would never see Mole again, he heard a little voice.

"Ratty, is that really you?"

"Mole, where are you?" Rat cried.

"I'm here in this hole under the big tree," Mole answered.

Rat found the hole and went inside.

"Oh, Ratty," cried Mole. "I've been so frightened. I thought I was going to die."

"It's all right, Mole. I'm here now," said Rat. "But why did you come here by yourself? You were very silly. The Wild Wood is a bad place when you're alone – I never come here by myself. But don't be afraid now. We'll soon be home again," and Rat laughed. "Come, Mole. We must start."

"Oh, Ratty," said Mole. "I'm very, very tired.

You must let me rest here. If I don't rest, I'll never reach home again."

"Oh, all right," said Rat.

So Mole sat down again on the dry leaves. Soon he was asleep.

Rat sat and waited.

After an hour Mole woke up. He said he was much better. They started for home. But when they got out of the hole everywhere looked different. It had snowed while Mole slept. Everything was white.

"Quickly," said Rat. "We must try to get home, but it's difficult because the snow has changed everything."

The two animals walked and walked but they couldn't find the way. They walked for more than two hours but they were still in the Wild Wood. They were both very tired.

Suddenly, Mole cried, "Oh, my leg! My leg!"

"Poor old Mole," said Rat. "Let me look at your leg. Yes, you've cut it on something. Sit down for a minute." He cleaned the cut as well as he could.

Then he looked at the piece of metal that had cut Mole's leg. "That's for cleaning shoes," he said. "And if there's a shoe cleaner, there must be a house near here." And he started to look in the snow.

"What *is* Rat thinking about?" Mole wondered to himself, but he didn't say anything.

After about ten minutes Rat cried, "What did I

tell you, Mole? Come and see!" And Rat showed Mole a little door. On the door were the words MR BADGER.

"Ratty," cried Mole, "How clever you are! Now I see what you were doing. Is this *really* Badger's house?"

"Yes," said Rat. "I think we're safe at last." He rang the door bell.

Chapter 5
Mr Badger

After a long time, Rat and Mole heard noises on the other side of the door. Then the door opened a little and a voice shouted, "Who's there?" The voice sounded very angry. "I don't want visitors. It's very late."

"Oh, please let us in, Badger," said Rat. "It's me, Rat, and my friend Mole. We've lost our way in the snow."

Badger's voice was very different when he spoke this time. "Ratty, my dear friend. Come in at once. You must be frozen."

How happy Rat and Mole were! The door closed behind them – they were safe at last.

Badger's house, like Mole's, was under the ground. He took the two cold animals down a long passage. There were a lot of doors. Badger opened one of them and there was the kitchen. There was a big open fire with soft chairs in front of it. In the middle of the room was a big table, and on the table was Badger's evening meal. Everything was warm and friendly. How different from the snow outside!

Rat and Mole sat down by the fire. They took off their wet coats and shoes. Then Badger cooked a hot dinner for his two friends. They all sat down to eat. Nobody spoke for a quarter of an hour – they were all eating! Then Badger asked Mole and Rat to tell him their story.

When Rat had finished, Badger said simply, "I'm glad you're here now." Mole thought what a good friend Badger was.

Then Badger wanted to know about life on the river. "How's old Toad?" he asked.

"Things are very bad," Rat answered sadly. "His car ran into a tree again last week. We want him to have a driver. But no, Toad must drive himself. He thinks he's the best driver in the world, but he really is dangerous, you know."

"How many cars has he had already?" Badger asked.

"Seven," said Rat. "He's been badly hurt three times, and the police are very angry with him. We must do something, Badger. We're his friends. We must stop him driving."

"Well, we can't do anything now," said Badger. "It's the middle of winter. We'll have to wait till spring comes. But when it gets warmer and the days get longer – then we'll do something. But now, my friends, it's bedtime. You're very tired, aren't you?"

"Not really," said Rat, but his eyes were closing.

"Don't get up early in the morning," Badger said as he showed them their beds. "You can have breakfast at any time."

The next morning both Rat and Mole slept very late. They were having breakfast when the doorbell rang. It was Otter.

"Good morning, good morning!" he shouted. "I'm glad you're all right. Everyone on the river bank was very frightened. No one knew where you were. They thought you were lost in the snow. But I thought you'd be here with Badger – and I was right. Now, what happened?"

So Rat and Mole told their story again. Poor Mole, he was quite frightened when he remembered the day before.

"Weren't you frightened, Otter? Did you come through the Wild Wood alone?" he asked quietly.

"Me? Frightened? No!" cried Otter. "I'm not frightened of anything or anyone. Can I have some breakfast, too? I'm very hungry."

So Mole cooked some eggs for Otter. While he was cooking, Otter and Rat had a long talk. They hadn't seen each other for a long time because of the winter.

Soon it was lunchtime and Badger came into the kitchen. After lunch Badger took Mole to see the rest of his house. Otter and Rat were still talking about their river.

Mole was surprised because Badger's house was so big.

"How did you make all this, Badger?" he asked.

"I didn't," said Badger. "These rooms were made by my mother and father and by their mothers and fathers. Badgers have lived here for many, many years."

"My house is under the ground, too," Mole said. "I like houses under the ground. They're so nice and warm."

"Yes," said Badger. "Do you like Toad's house? I don't. I know that Toad Hall is a beautiful house, but it's so cold in the winter. But down here in my house winter and summer are the same. Snow, wind, rain – I never notice them."

When they got back to the kitchen, Rat was walking up and down. He didn't like being under the ground.

"Mole," he said. "We really must go home. It'll soon be dark again. We don't want to be in the Wild Wood again tonight, do we?"

"Don't be frightened," said Otter. "I'm coming with you this time. I know the way."

"And I know the best way," said Badger. "The passages in my house go a long way. Come with me and I'll show you. You needn't go through the Wild Wood at all."

Badger led the three animals down many dark passages. After a long time they could feel cold air on their faces and at last they were outside again. They had left the Wild Wood far behind them. In front of them they could see the fields which went down to the river bank. They thanked Badger for his kindness.

Then Otter led the way back to the river. Very soon they were back at Rat's house. Both Rat and Mole were very glad to be home again.

Otter leads the way back to the river

Chapter 6
Mr Toad

The rest of the winter passed very quietly. At last, spring came and Rat and Mole began their usual busy life.

One morning in early summer Rat and Mole were having a late breakfast. They had been awake since six o'clock that morning. There was so much work. They were very hungry. The doorbell rang.

"Who can that be?" said Rat. "Go and see, Mole. You've finished your eggs and I haven't."

Mole went to open the door and Rat heard a cry of surprise.

"Who is it, Mole?" Rat shouted.

"It's Badger," said Mole, as he and Badger came into the room. "Isn't this wonderful?"

"Badger!" cried Rat. "How good to see you! Come and have some breakfast."

"Hello, Rat," Badger said quietly. "No, I won't have any breakfast, thank you. I'm here because the time has come."

"What time?" asked Rat.

"The time for us to change Toad," Badger answered. "I hear that he's still driving those silly cars. And one of the ducks has just told me that he's bought another new car."

"Oh, Badger, yes," Rat said. "Yes, we must teach Toad a lesson."

"And we must start today," Badger went on. "Summer is here and we must help our friend. I want you and Mole to come to Toad Hall with me."

"Yes, of course," Rat said. "Let's go now."

The three friends left at once. When they reached Toad Hall, they saw Toad's new car. It was big and red. Toad was coming down the steps of his house. He was wearing his driving clothes.

"Good morning, everyone!" he cried when he saw them. "Are you coming for a ride in my beautiful, new ... er ... er ..." Poor Toad had seen Badger's face. He knew that something was wrong.

"Take him inside," Badger said to Rat and Mole.

When the four animals were inside the house, Badger said, "Take those foolish driving clothes off, Toad. You won't need them today."

"I shan't," answered Toad rudely. "What's the meaning of this? How dare you come here and give me orders! This is my house."

"Take off those driving clothes, Mole," Badger ordered.

Toad still didn't know what was happening. He fought Rat and Mole but at last his driving coat and hat were off.

"Now, Toad," said Badger. "You know why we're here. You've behaved very badly. You've wasted your money on these foolish cars. The

The three friends see Toad and his new car

30

police are very angry with you. And you're a very dangerous driver. You must stop driving from today. I want to talk to you alone." And Badger took Toad into another room and closed the door.

"Huh! Talking isn't enough," said Rat. "Talking won't change Toad. Toad will *say* anything, won't he, Mole?"

Badger and Toad talked for a long time. After an hour the door opened and the two animals came out. Toad looked very unhappy.

"Sit down there, Toad," said Badger quite kindly. "You'll be pleased to hear this, my friends. Toad is very sorry about his past. He says that he will stop driving cars for ever."

There was a long silence. Rat noticed a smile in Toad's eyes – and he knew that Toad wasn't sorry at all.

At last Toad said rudely, "No, no, no. I'm *not* sorry. I love cars, and driving is the most wonderful thing in the world. I shan't stop."

"What?" cried Badger, very surprised. "You *are* a bad animal, Toad."

"What did I tell you, Mole?" Rat said quietly. "Toad will *say* anything."

Badger went on, "If you won't listen to words, Toad, we must make you change. You have often asked us to come and stay at Toad Hall. Well, now we're going to stay here. Mole, Rat, take Toad to his bedroom and lock the door. Then come back here. We must make our plans."

Toad was very, very angry. He fought hard, but at last Mole and Rat got him to his bedroom and locked the door.

"This is going to be difficult," said Badger when Mole and Rat came back. "Toad is very angry. It will take a long time to change him. One of us must be with him all the time, day and night. He must never be left alone."

And that is what Badger, Rat and Mole did. One of them slept in Toad's room at night. And all through the day one of them was with him. At first Toad was very rude and difficult. He shouted and cried and threw things round the room. But slowly he grew quieter.

One morning Rat went into Toad's room. Toad was still in bed. He looked ill. He was very quiet and sad.

Badger had slept in the room that night. "I don't know what's the matter with him," Badger said quietly. "The only thing he has said this morning is 'Leave me alone.' Be careful, Ratty. Toad can be very clever. He isn't usually so quiet. I think he's planning something. I must go now and have some breakfast." And he left the room.

"How are you today, Toad?" Rat asked.

Toad didn't answer at once. Then he said, "Thank you for asking, dear Ratty. I'm afraid I'm not well. I'm sorry I've been so difficult. But I don't think I'll be here very long. Then your work will end. I feel very ill."

"What are you talking about, Toad?" said Rat.

"Get out of bed. Let's play a game or something."

"Oh, Ratty, I don't think I can. I'll never play games again," Toad went on. His voice sounded smaller than before. "I don't want to be difficult but ..." he stopped for a minute and then went on, "I need the doctor, Ratty. Could you get him for me, please?"

"Why do you want the doctor?" Rat asked. "I don't think you're very ill." But Rat was beginning to be afraid. He looked closely at Toad. Yes, the poor animal seemed very sick.

"Perhaps I should get the doctor," Rat thought to himself. "Toad," he said. "If you're really ill, I'll get the doctor."

"Oh, dear Ratty," Toad said. "I'm afraid it may be too late."

When he heard Toad's words, Rat knew that he had to go at once. Perhaps poor Toad was dying.

"Don't say foolish things," he said quietly. "I'll go for the doctor at once."

As soon as Rat had left the room, Toad jumped out of bed. He wasn't ill! He was going to be free at last! He sang a little song as he dressed. Rat hadn't remembered to lock the door behind him. So Toad went quietly out of his room and left the house. No one saw him.

At lunchtime Rat had to tell Badger and Mole the story. They were not pleased.

"I told you to be careful," said Badger angrily.

Toad asks Rat to get the doctor

"And now he has made fools of us. What are we going to do? I think we should stay here for a few days. Toad may come back – but he may not," he added.

By lunchtime Toad was already five miles away from Toad Hall. He was free and he was happy. He thought he was very clever.

"I fooled them! I fooled them!" he said to himself. "Poor Ratty. The others will be very angry when they know."

Soon he reached a small town.

"I'm hungry," he thought. "I must find a place where I can eat."

Then he saw a place across the road. It was called *The Black Horse*. He walked in and ordered some lunch. While he was eating, he heard a noise outside. *"Poop! Poop!"* He had heard that noise before – it was a motor car!

The people who owned the car came into *The Black Horse*. They sat down and ordered some food. By now, Toad had finished his meal. The noise of the car had made him very excited.

"I must go and look at it," he thought to himself. So he paid for his lunch and went outside.

There was the car – beautiful and new! Toad looked at it for a long time. How wonderful it was!

"I wonder if it starts easily?" he thought. The next minute he had opened the door and was sitting in the front. He was so excited! He didn't know what he was doing. He started the car and drove off.

"What a good life!" he cried happily.

But his happiness didn't last. The police caught him about twenty miles away.

The next day Toad had to go before the judge. The judge was very angry with him.

"Toad," he said. "You have been a very bad Toad for three reasons. Firstly, you stole a motor car. Secondly, you drove that car very dangerously. Thirdly, you were very rude to the police when they stopped you. You must go to prison for twenty years."

Poor Toad! He looked so unhappy. Twenty years is a very long time.

Chapter 7
Toad's adventures

When Toad arrived in the dark, cold prison he threw himself on the floor. He cried and cried and cried.

"This is the end of Toad. The end of everything." he cried. "I've been very bad. They will never set me free. I've been so foolish. My dear friends won't remember me. I wish I'd listened to Badger and Ratty and Mole. They were right and I was wrong." And he began to cry again.

But life in prison wasn't so bad. The man who looked after the prison had a pretty daughter. She liked animals and she felt very sorry for Toad.

One day she said to her father. "Please let me talk to Toad. He seems so unhappy. And I'd like to take him some good food. He isn't eating enough and he looks quite ill."

Her father said that she could. And so the girl went to see Toad.

"Good morning, Toad," she said. "I've brought you some good food. Sit up and try to eat it."

Toad didn't answer. He lay on the floor in silence. So the girl left the food and went away. The food filled the room with a good smell. Soon Toad had to eat it! And he began to feel happier. Perhaps everything was not lost.

When the girl came back that evening Toad looked much better. This time she had brought him some tea, some fresh bread and a cake. While Toad ate, the girl sat and talked to him.

"Tell me about Toad Hall," she said. "I've heard that it's very beautiful."

"Toad Hall," said Toad, "is the most beautiful house in England. It's very old. Parts of it are more than four hundred years old. But inside everything is new and wonderful." And Toad laughed for the first time in weeks. The girl saw that he was better.

After that, the girl came to visit Toad three times every day. Each time she brought him food and stayed to talk to him. They had many long talks and Toad told her all about Toad Hall and his life there.

The girl felt very sorry for Toad. "He shouldn't be in prison. It was wrong to steal that car, but he's sorry now," she thought. Then she had an idea.

The next time she saw Toad, she said, "Toad, listen. I have an idea. I have an aunt who's a washerwoman. She does the washing for the prison. She takes the washing every Monday morning and she brings it back on Friday. You've told me that you're very rich. She is very poor. Perhaps if you give her some money, she will give you her clothes. Then you can leave the prison. Everyone will think you're the washerwoman."

"Well," said Toad slowly. He didn't like the idea of wearing a washerwoman's clothes. But he didn't like the idea of being in prison for twenty years. And so he quickly said, "You are a clever girl. That's a very good idea. Today is Thursday. Can I see your aunt when she comes tomorrow?"

"Yes, of course, Toad," the girl answered. "I must go now, but I'll see you tomorrow."

The next afternoon the girl came into Toad's room with her aunt. Toad paid the washerwoman twenty pounds and she gave him her clothes.

"You look just like my aunt," the girl laughed as Toad put on the clothes. "No one will know that you're really Mr Toad."

Toad didn't like this at all, but he knew that he had to keep quiet.

And so Toad left the prison. A few people talked to him and said, "Good afternoon," but no one stopped him.

At last he was outside the prison. He was free again! He knew that he had to get away from the prison quickly, but he didn't know the way home. Then he heard a train. "Aha!" he cried. "That's the answer!"

But when he put his hand where his money usually was – he couldn't find it. He had left his money in his other clothes!

"Oh dear, what am I going to do?" Toad asked himself. He couldn't get on the train because he hadn't got any money. He began to cry.

Just then the train arrived. The driver saw Toad crying.

"Hello, washerwoman," he said. "What's the matter? You look very sad."

"Oh dear!" cried Toad. "I've lost all my money and I can't get on your train. I must get home tonight. If I don't, my children will have no food. I don't know what to do."

"Well," said the driver kindly. "If you'll wash some clothes for me, I'll give you a ride on my train. I ought not to do this, but I feel very sorry for you. Come, get up here beside me."

Toad felt better at once and he jumped up on to the train.

The train left. Toad was on his way home at last. After many miles the driver suddenly said, "Something's wrong. We're the last train this evening, but I can see another train behind us. It's going very fast, too."

"Oh, no!" thought Toad. "The police are coming to catch me."

The other train came nearer. "I can see a lot of policemen," said the driver. "I wonder what they're doing?"

Then Toad had to tell the driver. "Help me! Help me!" he cried. "Dear driver, I'll tell you everything. I'm not a washerwoman. I haven't got any children. I'm Mr Toad of Toad Hall. I've just run away from prison. If those policemen catch me, I'll have to go back to prison for twenty years."

"But why were you in prison?" the driver asked.

"Oh, I hadn't done anything very bad," said Toad. "I took a car while its owners were having lunch. I didn't really *steal* it. I was going to give it back. And now I'm sorry about it. I'm telling you the truth – I really am."

"All right," said the driver. "You've been a very bad Toad, but I can see that you're sorry. So I won't give you to the police. I hate to see you so unhappy. But what are we going to do? Our train is very long and heavy. We can't go very fast. But the train behind us is small and light. They can go very fast." He thought for a minute and then he went on. "I know. Listen carefully, Toad. Soon we'll come to a long dark tunnel through a hill. On the other side of the tunnel there's a wood. I'll go very slowly there and you can jump out. You can hide in the wood. Then I'll go very fast. The police will be in the tunnel. They won't see you when you jump out. They'll think that you're still on this train."

"Thank you, thank you!" Toad cried.

"Are you ready?" the driver asked. "You must jump when I say."

They went through the tunnel very fast. Then the driver slowed the train and shouted, "Jump!"

Toad jumped. He landed safely on the bank and ran quickly into the wood. Two minutes later

The police try to catch Toad in a train

he saw the second train go by. He laughed and laughed.

But he soon stopped laughing. It was very late and very cold. He didn't know where he was and he was very, very hungry. He was also frightened. The wood was so quiet and dark.

"I'll stay here until morning," he said to himself. He found a hole under a tree and climbed into it. He lay down and tried to sleep.

Chapter 8
More of Toad's adventures

The next morning Toad woke up very early because he was so cold. For a minute he couldn't remember where he was. Then he thought, "I'm free! I'm free!"

He started to walk, but he didn't know the way to Toad Hall. There was no one to ask because it was so early in the morning. So he started to walk along a small country road. "It must go somewhere," he said to himself. "All roads go somewhere."

Soon he came to a river. There was a boat on the river. A horse was pulling the boat.

"Good morning," a woman on the boat called to Toad. "It's a lovely morning, isn't it?"

"Yes, it is," said Toad sadly. "But everything's going wrong today. As you see, I'm a washer-woman, but I've had to leave my job. My married daughter needs me and I must go to her. I've left all my other children at home and there's no one to look after them. And now I've lost my money and I've lost my way. What shall I do?" Toad cried.

"Where does your married daughter live?" the boat woman asked kindly.

"She lives near the river," Toad answered. "Near a fine house called Toad Hall. Have you heard of it?"

"Yes, of course I have," the woman said. "And I'm going very near there. Get in the boat and I'll take you."

"Oh, thank you, thank you," cried Toad and he got into the boat.

"So you're a washerwoman?" asked the boat woman after a few minutes. "I wonder if you would help me? I have a lot of dirty clothes but I haven't time to wash them. My husband is very lazy and he's gone away for the day. I want to do the washing but I have to look after the boat. Will you wash the clothes for me?"

"Er ... er ... er," Toad didn't know what to say. Then he thought to himself. "Anyone can wash clothes. I'll try."

So he got the dirty clothes, the hot water and the soap. But washing clothes wasn't easy. Poor Toad! He couldn't get the clothes clean. He tried and tried for nearly an hour. He got quite angry with himself and with the clothes.

Suddenly he heard the woman. She was laughing at him. "I've been watching you!" she cried. "You don't know how to wash clothes. I don't think you're a real washerwoman." And she laughed again.

This made Toad really angry. "You bad unkind woman!" he cried rudely. "How dare you laugh at me! No, of course I'm not a washerwoman. I'm Mr Toad of Toad Hall!"

The boat woman looked at him very carefully. "Ugh!" she cried. "A dirty toad! And on my boat!

Get off at once." And she took hold of Toad's leg and threw him into the river – SPLASH!

Toad was very, very angry now. The water was very cold. His washerwoman's clothes made swimming very difficult. But at last he reached the bank. He saw the boat woman on her boat – she was still laughing at him. He wanted to hurt her. But what could he do? Suddenly he saw the horse and he had an idea.

He ran to the horse and took the rope from around its head. Then he jumped on to the horse's back. The next minute he was riding very fast across the fields. He looked back once and saw the boat woman.

"Stop! Stop! Stop!" she cried.

"Oh, no, I shan't," he answered.

The horse couldn't go very fast, but Toad didn't mind. After some time he came to a big field. In the corner of the field he saw a caravan. A man was cooking some food on a fire outside the caravan. The food smelled wonderful.

"How hungry I am," thought Toad. "I must eat something." But how? He hadn't got any money.

As Toad passed the caravan the man spoke to him, "Do you want to sell that horse?" he asked.

Toad was very surprised – and pleased. He hadn't thought of that idea. He needed the money very badly.

"What?" he said. "Do I want to sell my horse? No, of course I don't. How can I work

Toad rides away on the boat woman's horse

without a horse? But –" he added, "if I sold him, how much would you give me?"

"Four pounds," the man answered.

"Four pounds!" cried Toad. "I paid more than that for him. I'd want ten pounds. He's a very good horse."

"Five pounds then," the man went on. "And no more."

Toad really was very hungry. He had to have some money. The man's food smelled very good, so he said, "I'll take seven pounds for the horse if you give me some breakfast. Now, what do you say?"

"All right," said the man slowly, "if I must." He gave Toad the money and then he went into his caravan. He brought out a plate. Then he gave Toad some breakfast.

Toad started to eat. It was the best breakfast of his life. He ate and ate and ate. At last he couldn't eat any more. He thanked the man and said goodbye.

He started to walk towards Toad Hall. He was very happy and he sang as he walked. "What a clever Toad I am!" he thought to himself. "I've fooled everybody."

After an hour or more he began to feel tired. Then he heard a car behind him. "I'll ask the driver to take me to Toad Hall if he's going that way," Toad thought. "How good to be in a car again."

He waved at the car. It stopped. But when

Toad saw the car clearly his happiness left him. "That's the car I stole from outside *The Black Horse*," he thought. "And the same people are in it. Oh, what shall I do?"

It was too late to go back. He sat down at the side of the road. "Everything is finished," he thought. "They'll take me to the police and then I'll be back in prison again! Oh, foolish Toad, why didn't you travel at night?"

Two men got out of the car. "Oh, dear," one of them said. "This poor washerwoman looks very ill. What shall we do?"

"Let's take her to the next village. She must have friends there. Perhaps they can help," the other man said.

They gently put Toad into the front of the car. They sounded so friendly and kind that Toad was less frightened. He opened one eye and then the other.

"Are you feeling better?" the driver asked.

"Yes, thank you," Toad answered. "I'm much better now."

The driver started the car and for a time Toad didn't say anything. But at last he couldn't keep quiet any longer.

"Please, sir," he said. "I've never driven a car, but I've always wanted to drive. I've been watching you and it doesn't look very difficult. Do you think I could try to drive – just for a little way?"

The driver laughed and the other man said,

49

"Let her drive. The road is quiet."

And so they let Toad drive. At first he drove quite carefully, but then he went faster and faster and faster.

"Be careful, washerwoman!" shouted the two men. But Toad didn't listen.

"Ho, ho!" he cried. "This is wonderful! I'm not a washerwoman. I'm clever Mr Toad. The best driver in the world. You can't stop me now!"

"Toad – *the* Toad?" cried the two men. "The Toad who stole our car? Stop, stop at once! We'll take you back to the police."

But Toad didn't want to go back to prison so he turned the wheel suddenly. The car went off the road. It crossed a field and stopped suddenly against a tree. Toad was thrown out. He got up and started to run away very fast. The two men were still inside the car. They couldn't get out because the doors were broken.

Toad ran and ran. Then he looked behind him. Oh, no! The men had got out of the car. They were following him. They were running very fast, too. By now Toad was tired.

"I can't run any more!" he thought. "They'll catch me. Their legs are longer than mine. What shall I do? I'm a foolish Toad. Why do I do these silly things?"

Suddenly – SPLASH! Toad fell into some very deep water. He hadn't seen the river. He tried to swim to the bank, but he was too tired. Then he felt a hand which pushed him towards a hole in the bank. He also heard a voice which he knew very well.

"Good morning, Toad. Where have you come from?"

It was Ratty.

Chapter 9
Toad sees his friends again

Rat pushed Toad out of the water and into his hole.

"Oh, Ratty," said Toad. "I'm so glad to see you. I've had so many adventures and I've been so clever. I've fooled everyone. I must tell you everything."

"Wait a minute, Toad," said Ratty. "First, you must take off those wet clothes. I must say, you look very silly. Why are you wearing a washer-woman's clothes? No, don't tell me now. No more talking. Go and change at once."

When Toad came back, lunch was on the table. While they ate, Toad told Rat about his adventures. He talked mostly about his own cleverness. He was boasting again! Rat said nothing for a long time. Then at last he held up his hand.

"I don't want to hurt you, Toad. And I know that you've only just come home. But you must stop boasting. All this talk is foolish. You are not clever. You've behaved very, very badly. You've been in prison. Does that mean nothing to you? How do you think Mole and I feel? We don't like having a friend who's been in prison. People say unkind things about it."

Poor Toad! Half of him knew that Rat was right. But the other half of him didn't want to believe it. He had had fun on his adventures. In the end, the good half won and Toad said very quietly, "You're right, Ratty. I've been very foolish. But from now on, I'm going to be good. I don't like cars any more. The trouble this morning taught me a lesson. And I've just had a wonderful idea – motorboats!"

Here Ratty began to look very angry.

"No, Ratty, don't be angry with me," Toad went on. "It was only an idea. I didn't mean it. I won't say any more. Let's have some coffee. We'll talk about something different."

While they were having coffee, Toad said, "I think I'll walk down to Toad Hall next. I must get some clean clothes and I want to see the old place again."

"Walk down to Toad Hall?" cried Rat. "But you can't. Haven't you heard, Toad?"

"Heard what?" asked Toad, surprised. "Tell me, tell me, Ratty. Quick! What's happened? What haven't I heard?"

"About the stoats and weasels from the Wild Wood," Rat answered. "They've taken Toad Hall."

Poor Toad! Big tears appeared in his eyes. He began to cry, very quietly at first. "Go on, Ratty," he said sadly. "Tell me everything. I must know."

"Oh, Toad," said Rat. "I don't want to tell you, but I must." He stopped for a minute and then went on. "After you'd left ... er ... after you'd gone to prison – everyone thought you wouldn't come back. Well, not everyone. Mole, Badger and I said that you would come back, but the other animals didn't believe us. Mole and Badger – your best friends, Toad, I hope you'll always remember that – Mole and Badger stayed at Toad Hall to look after the house. Then one dark cold night, the stoats and weasels from the Wild Wood went to Toad Hall. They had guns and knives and sticks. They threw Badger and Mole out of the house. Badger and Mole fought very bravely, but there were only two of them. They hadn't got any guns or sticks or knives. And there were hundreds of stoats and weasels. That's the sad story. The stoats and weasels have been living in Toad Hall ever since that night. They're eating your food, drinking your drink, sleeping in your beds. The place is very dirty and many of your things are broken. I'm sorry that I had to tell you."

"My poor house," cried Toad. "My beautiful Toad Hall. What am I going to do? I'd like to go there this minute. I want to fight those stoats and weasels."

"But you can't," Rat said. "There are too many of them. We've tried to get into the house, but there are stoats everywhere – in the garden, by the river, on the road. They all have guns. We can't get near."

"I don't care," cried Toad. "I'm going to try now." And he jumped up and left Rat's house before Rat could stop him.

Toad came back in an hour. He looked very sad.

"What did I tell you?" Rat said. "We can't do anything. We can only wait."

"You were right, Ratty," Toad said quietly. "A stoat stopped me at the gate. He said that he would shoot me if I went into the garden. So I went round to the back of the house. But the same thing happened. What are we going to do?" He was almost crying.

"First, we'll have some tea," Rat said kindly. "Then we'll wait for Badger and Mole. They may have some new ideas."

"Yes, Ratty," said Toad. "How are Mole and Badger? I didn't ask you about them."

"Why didn't you, Toad?" Rat said. "They're your best friends. And they've thought of you. Every day since the stoats and weasels took Toad Hall, Mole and Badger have been there. They've watched very carefully. They know everything about the stoats and weasels. They can't *do* anything yet, but they *know* everything. Really Toad, you should be more thankful."

"Oh, Ratty," said Toad. "I'm so sorry. I am thankful – I really am, but life's been so difficult . . ." and Toad started to cry again.

"Stop crying, Toad," said Rat. "It doesn't help. Have some tea."

When they had finished their tea, the doorbell rang. It was Badger. He was wet and cold and hungry. He didn't seem very surprised or pleased to see Toad.

"Hello, Toad," he said. "I'm hungry. " And he sat down to eat his tea. He didn't say anything more until he had finished.

Then Mole came in. He too was cold, wet and hungry. But he was very glad to see Toad.

"Good afternoon, Toad. It's good to see you again! How did you get out of prison? You must be very clever to get away from the police. I want to hear all about your adventures."

Toad was just going to tell Mole all about his adventures when Rat stopped him.

"Be quiet, Toad," he said angrily. "We don't want to hear any more boasting. You've behaved very badly and you know it. And don't ask him any more questions, Mole. He isn't clever. He's very silly. Now, Badger and Mole, what's happened at Toad Hall?"

"I'm afraid," said Mole, "that Badger and I can't find any way into the place. There are stoats with guns everywhere. They laugh when they see us. And they say rude things about you, Toad. It makes me very angry."

"But what are we going to do?" Badger asked. "Toad has come home and he needs his house."

Rat, Mole and Toad all began to speak at the same time. They all had different ideas.

"Oh, be quiet, all of you!" Badger shouted. There was a sudden silence. "I want you to listen very carefully. We can't fight the stoats and weasels. There are too many of them and there are only four of us. But there is another way. I'm going to tell you something very important. Only I know about it."

"Oh, ho, ho!" cried Toad excitedly.

"You mustn't tell anyone, Toad," said Badger. "If you tell anyone, we're lost. Do you understand?"

"Yes, Badger," said Toad quietly.

"There's a tunnel under the ground," Badger went on. "It goes from the river bank right into the middle of Toad Hall."

"Oh, no, Badger. That can't be true," Toad laughed. "I've lived in Toad Hall all my life and I've never heard of an underground tunnel. My father never told me about a tunnel."

"No, he didn't," said Badger. "Your father knew you too well. But he told me about it. He said that I must tell you only if you were in real danger. Our present difficulties are so bad that I can tell you now."

"Oh, dear," said Toad. "I'm afraid my father was right. But I'm not such a bad Toad, am I? I'm kind to people and they like me, don't they?"

No one answered Toad. Badger went on. "I've just learned something else. Otter tells me that there's going to be a big party at Toad Hall tomorrow night. The Head Weasel is twenty-one years old tomorrow. This is my plan. The tunnel comes out in a room next to the room where the party will be. We can surprise all the weasels. The stoats will be outside the house with their guns, but the weasels won't have their guns with them at the party. And so we four will be able to beat them easily. Without their guns and sticks the weasels aren't very brave."

"Well done, Badger!" cried Rat, Mole and Toad.

"So that's what we shall do. And now we must go to bed. We must rest as much as possible. Tomorrow will be a difficult day. Goodnight, my friends." And Badger left the room.

Toad slept very well that night. It was late when he got up the next morning. Rat, Mole and Badger had already had breakfast. Mole had gone out. Badger was reading. Rat was very busy. He was gathering together guns, sticks and knives for the four friends.

"A gun for Badger. A gun for Mole. A gun for Toad and a gun for me," he said quietly to himself. "A stick for Badger. A stick for Mole. A stick for Toad and a stick for me."

"Ratty," said Badger. "We don't need all these guns and knives and things. A stick will be enough."

"But we may need them," Rat answered. "It's better to have too much than too little, isn't it?"

After lunch Mole still had not come back. The other three animals sat down to wait. The afternoon seemed endless.

Chapter 10
The battle for Toad Hall

Late in the afternoon Mole come in. He was looking very pleased with himself.

"Where have you been, Mole?" Rat asked.

"I've had a wonderful afternoon, Ratty," Mole cried excitedly. "I've been to Toad Hall!"

"But why?" Rat asked. "I hope you haven't done anything foolish or dangerous."

"Oh, no," said Mole. "I was quite safe and I've had a lot of fun."

"Tell us about it," said Toad. He wished that he had gone with Mole.

"I found Toad's washerwoman's clothes this morning," Mole began. "And I had a good idea. So I put them on and I went up to Toad Hall. I asked the stoats and weasels if they had any washing. They all said no, they never had any washing. They really are dirty animals, aren't they? I stayed to talk to some of the stoats but a weasel came out. He told me to go away. He said I was wasting the stoats' time. I laughed at him and said, 'Go away? It won't be me who goes away soon. Soon you stoats and weasels will have to go away!'"

"Oh, Mole, what have you done?" cried Rat. "They will be waiting for us now."

"No, Rat. Wait a minute," Mole went on. "I told him that I worked for Mr Badger. I said that

I'd heard that a hundred brave, strong badgers were going to go to Toad Hall. I said that they were going to throw out all the stoats and weasels. I also told them that hundreds of rats and toads and moles were coming. The stoats and weasels looked very frightened. They all started to talk at the same time – everyone was giving orders."

"Oh, Mole," cried Toad. "You are a fool!"

"No, Toad," said Badger quietly, "Mole has done a very clever thing. Well done, Mole!"

Toad and Rat still didn't know what Badger meant. But they knew that Badger was always right, so they didn't say anything.

They had an early meal that evening. When it was dark, they all met at Rat's front door. Rat gave each of them a gun, a stick and a knife. Then Badger took a light and said, "Follow me! Mole first because I'm very pleased with him. Then Rat and then Toad. And you must behave, Toad. If you don't, we'll send you back. Do you understand?"

"Yes, Badger," said Toad quietly. He didn't like being last but he couldn't say anything.

First, they walked along the river bank for a little way. Then Badger went into a hole in the bank. Mole and Rat followed him easily but Toad fell into the river – SPLASH! Mole and Rat pulled him out – he was very wet and cold. Badger was angry.

"I told you to behave, Toad," he said. "One

more foolish thing and we'll leave you behind."

At last they were inside the tunnel. It was cold and dark and wet. Poor Toad, he was still very wet and he couldn't walk as fast as the others.

"Quickly, Toad!" shouted Rat from in front.

But Toad came too quickly! He was afraid that he would be left behind. So he ran to catch the others – but he ran too fast in the darkness. He ran into Rat, who pushed Mole, who made Badger fall over!

This time Badger was really angry. "Go back at once, Toad!" he shouted. "We don't want you with us!"

Poor Toad began to cry. He wanted to be with them when they got to Toad Hall. Rat and Mole felt sorry for him and Rat said, "Let him come with us, Badger. I know he'll be good from now on. And we're going to *his* house, aren't we?"

So Toad stayed with them.

After a long time, they heard a noise above their heads. It sounded a long way away. People were singing and shouting and laughing.

"They're having a good party," Badger said. "Good, they won't hear us."

Soon the tunnel began to go up. The next minute they got out of the tunnel through a door in the floor. They were in the room next to the party! There was a lot of noise.

"Follow me!" cried Badger to his friends.

"The time has come!" And he threw open the door.

The four friends ran into the middle of the party. They used their guns and their sticks and their knives. Crash! A weasel fell to the floor. Bang! Another weasel hit his head against a table. The four friends fought very bravely. The weasels were very, very frightened. They thought that there were hundreds of moles, rats, badgers and toads. They didn't know that there were only four! They were too surprised.

Many of the weasels tried to run away, but the doors and windows weren't wide enough for them all. Some weasels hid behind the curtains. Other weasels hid under the tables and chairs. But the four friends found them all and sent them running.

Soon the fight was over. Toad had hit the Head Weasel very hard. The weasels didn't have a leader any more. Badger was right – without their guns and sticks the weasels weren't brave. They had all run away.

After they had gone, Badger said, "I'm hungry. What about some food, Toad? We've all worked hard."

The four animals found a lot of food in the dining room. The weasels and stoats hadn't finished their meal.

"You have your house again, Toad. I hope that you're thankful," said Badger while they were eating.

The weasels run and hide from the four friends

"Oh, I am, I am," said Toad. "Thank you all a thousand times."

Badger's next question was, "Where are we all going to sleep? Mole, will you and Toad go and get some beds ready?"

Toad didn't like the idea. And he didn't like Badger giving him orders in his own house. But he didn't say anything. He was so happy to be home at last. Mole and Toad came back ten minutes later.

"There are four clean beds," said Mole. "That will be enough for tonight. But, oh dear, the house is dirty and so many things are broken. We'll have a lot of work tomorrow."

"We'll think about that in the morning," said Badger. "Now it's bedtime."

Chapter 11
Toad's big party

The next morning Toad slept very late as usual. The other three animals had already had breakfast when Toad came downstairs. Mole and Rat were sitting in the garden in the sunshine. They were talking and laughing a lot. Badger was inside, reading quietly. He looked up when Toad came into the room.

"Good morning, Toad," he said. "I'm glad you're here at last. I want to talk to you about your party."

"Party? What party?" asked Toad, surprised.

"The party for all your friends," Badger said. "You're home again and so you must have a party. It would be very rude if you didn't give a party."

"Oh, I see," said Toad. "Yes, of course we must have a party. What fun! When shall we have it? Next Saturday?"

"Mole, Rat and I think we should have the party tonight," Badger said.

"Oh," said Toad. "That doesn't give me much time."

"No, it doesn't," Badger went on. "You must write the invitations at once."

"But I haven't had breakfast yet," Toad said. "And I'm very hungry."

"Oh, all right," said Badger. "But be quick!

Here's some paper and a pen. I want you to ask all your friends to the party. While you're writing the invitations, I'll order the food and drink."

"But Badger," Toad said sadly. "I want to go and look at my house and garden this morning. I haven't seen them for a long time. I don't want to stay inside. It's such a beautiful morning. I don't want to write hundreds of invitations – not today, please."

Badger was beginning to look angry. Toad noticed it and went on quickly, "Oh, but of course I'll write the invitations at once. You know best, Badger. You're always right. I can look at my garden any day. I must do what you say. You've been very kind to me. You've helped me get my house back."

"Well said, Toad," said Badger and he left the room.

Toad went to his writing desk. Suddenly, he had an idea – and he started to laugh.

"I'll write the invitations," he thought to himself. "And then tonight I'll make a speech. I'll tell everyone about me – the brave and clever Toad. Toad, who beat all the stoats and weasels. Toad, who fooled the police, the boat woman and the owners of that car. I really am the cleverest Toad in the world! And after I've written the invitations, I'll write some songs. I'll sing the songs at the party tonight." He was very pleased with himself!

He sat down and began to write. He worked all morning.

---- INVITATION ----

Please come to a party tonight at Toad Hall. Toad will make three speeches about his adventures and he will sing some songs.

When Toad had finished the invitations, he gave them to the postman.

"Take these invitations to all my friends," he told the postman. "And be quick! We haven't much time."

Then he went to his bedroom to write some songs.

The four animals met for lunch at one o'clock. No one talked very much, but after the meal, Badger turned to Toad and said, "Come with me Toad. We'll go into the other room. I want to talk to you. Please come with us, Rat."

Inside the room, Badger went on, "Now Toad, I want you to listen carefully. We've seen your silly invitations. We stopped the postman before lunch. The invitations are no good. You must write some more – simple ones. There must be no songs and no speeches at the party tonight.

Your friends already know the story of your adventures. You needn't tell them again. Remember – no speeches and no songs."

"Not even one little song?" Toad asked sadly.

"No, not one," Rat answered. But he saw Toad's sad face, and he felt sorry for his friend. "Toad, you must understand. In the past you have always talked too much about yourself and your cleverness. No one likes listening to boasting. Your friends like you very much, but they don't always like your talk. From now on you must stop talking about yourself so much."

"I know you're right, Ratty," Toad cried. "I know I'm a foolish Toad. I know I talk too much about myself. I'll try to change. I really will try. And now I'll go and write some new invitations." And Toad left the room.

"Oh, Badger," cried Rat. "I hate being unkind to Toad."

"I know, I know," Badger answered. "So do I. But someone has to teach him. We're his friends. We have to tell him."

At last, evening came. Toad's friends came to Toad Hall for the party. Toad was still in his bedroom. He felt a little sad. Rat and Badger's words had hurt him deeply. Suddenly he began to laugh quietly.

"I know my friends are right," he said. "I must change my ways. But before I change, I'm going to sing one last song – one of the songs I wrote this morning. I won't sing it at the party –

that would make Badger very angry. I'll sing it now." And so he sang *When Toad came home!* – his last song.

Then he went down to meet his friends.

"Hooray! Hooray!" they all shouted when he came into the room. "Hooray! for our good friend Toad!"

Everyone wanted to hear about Toad's adventures, but he didn't tell them. Someone said how clever he was. Another person said how brave he was. But Toad simply answered, "Oh, it was nothing." Toad had changed!

The party was wonderful. Badger had ordered the best food and drink. Everyone had fun. There was a lot of talking and laughing.

During the evening Otter asked Toad to make a speech. But Toad said, "No, no. I really can't. I have nothing to say, my friends." Toad had changed!

After the big party the four friends went back to their old way of life. Badger went back to his house in the Wild Wood. Rat and Mole went back to Rat's house by the river. Toad lived quietly at Toad Hall. He sent a present to the pretty girl at the prison. He wrote a thankful letter to the train driver. And he even bought a new horse for the boat woman! And he did not buy any more cars or motorboats!

Toad sings his last song

Questions

Questions on each chapter

1 The river bank
1 Where did Mole live?
2 Where did Water Rat come from?
3 Who are Rat's friends on the river bank?
4 Who did Rat introduce Mole to?
5 Why did Rat's boat turn over? (Because . . .)

2 Mole meets Toad
1 How did Rat and Mole go to Toad's house?
2 What did Toad boast about?
3 What did Toad want Rat and Mole to do?

3 The open road
1 Why didn't Rat want to go home?
  (Because it wasn't safe . . .)
2 Who did all the work in the morning?
3 What was the "thing" in the cloud of dust?
4 Why won't Toad go to the police? (Because . . .)

4 The Wild Wood
1 When were Rat and Mole lazy?
2 What was the name of the dark wood?
3 How did Rat know where Mole had gone? (He saw . . .)
4 Where did Rat find Mole?
5 What cut Mole's leg?

5 Mr Badger
1 Which room did they go into in Badger's house?
2 Why were the police angry with Toad?
3 When did Otter come?
4 Why does Mole like houses under the ground?
5 Where did the passages in Badger's house end?

6 *Mr Toad*
  1 Where did Badger want to go with Rat and Mole?
  2 What was Toad wearing?
  3 Who locked Toad in his room?
  4 Why did Rat leave Toad's room?
  5 Where was Toad when he heard the car?
  6 How long must Toad be in prison?

7 *Toad's adventures*
  1 Who brought Toad some good food?
  2 How many times a day did the girl visit Toad?
  3 What was the girl's aunt?
  4 Why didn't Toad have any money?
  5 How did the police try to catch Toad?
  6 Where did Toad jump off the train?

8 *More of Toad's adventures*
  1 What did the boat woman ask Toad to do?
  2 What did she do to him?
  3 What did the man pay for the horse?
  4 What happened to the car?
  5 Who pulled Toad out of the river?

9 *Toad sees his friends again*
  1 What was Toad's "wonderful idea"?
  2 What happened at Toad Hall?
  3 Where did the tunnel go?
  4 Who told Badger about the party?
  5 What was the reason for the party?

10 *The battle for Toad Hall*
  1 What clothes did Mole put on?
  2 What noise did the friends hear?
  3 What did the weasels think?
  4 Where did the four friends sleep?

11 *Toad's big party*
  1 What were the invitations for?
  2 Who stopped the postman?
  3 When did Toad sing his last song?
  4 What two things did Toad NOT do at the party?
  5 What did Toad never do again?

Questions on the whole story

These are harder questions. Read the Introduction, and think hard about the questions before you answer them. Some of them ask for your opinion, and there is no fixed answer.

1 Mole:
  a Where did he live before he met Water Rat?
  b Where does he live after he meets Water Rat?
  c He is sometimes foolish. Can you give an example?
  d He is interested in everything. Can you give an example?
  e He is very kind-hearted. Can you give an example?

2 Water Rat:
  a Where is his house?
  b Rat does things that real water rats don't do. Can you give three examples?
  c Can you give an example of his kindness to Mole?
  d What does he think of Toad?
  e Can you give an example of his kindness to Toad?

3 Badger:
  a Where does he live?
  b He is brave. Can you give an example?
  c He is a good friend to Toad. Can you give an example?
  d The first time Mole saw him, Badger turned round and walked away. Why?

4 Toad:
  a Can you give two examples of the way he boasts?
  b He sometimes behaves very badly. Can you give two examples?
  c He doesn't mean to be bad. Can you prove it?
  d He seems to be quite brave. Can you give an example?

5 Say which of these is nearest to your feelings about Toad [A. I like him very much. – B. I half-like him. – C. I dislike him.] Can you give reasons for choosing A or B or C?

6 Do you know a person (in real life, or in another book, or in a film, etc) who is like, or rather like, Toad? Describe that person to show how he or she is like Toad.

New words

adventure
something that happens
and excites you

boast
talk about your own
greatness

caravan
a small house on wheels

idea
a thought in the mind

judge
a person who hears both
sides in a question of law

lunch
the meal that we eat in the
middle of the day

party
a meal and fun for several
people

prison
a place where those who
break the law are locked up

row
use oars to move a boat

rude
rough in ways of behaving
or speaking

speech
a long talk to a group of
people

tunnel
an underground passage

washerwoman
a woman who does
washing, washes clothes
for money

a wood
a small forest